Usborne

Little Coloring
Dinosaurs

Illustrated by Jenny Brown

Words by Kirsteen Robson

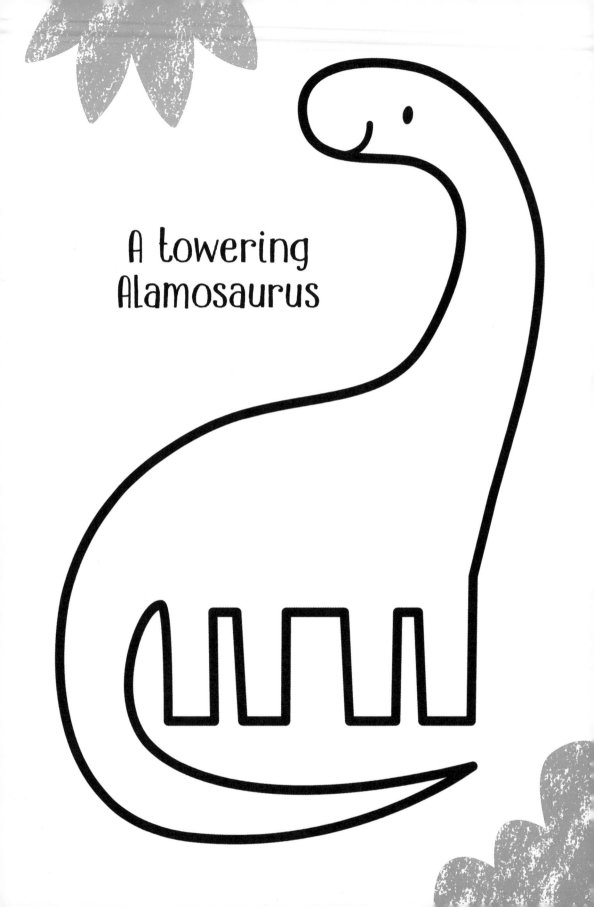

A towering
Alamosaurus

A swooping
Pteranodon

A noisy
Parasaurolophus

A pointy-plated Stegosaurus

A powerful
Tyrannosaurus
rex

A swimming
Muraenosaurus

A dome-headed
Stegoceras

A long-horned
Triceratops

A feathery
Velociraptor

A gentle Iguanodon

A spiky-headed Styracosaurus

A gigantic
Giganotosaurus

A snapping
Liopleurodon

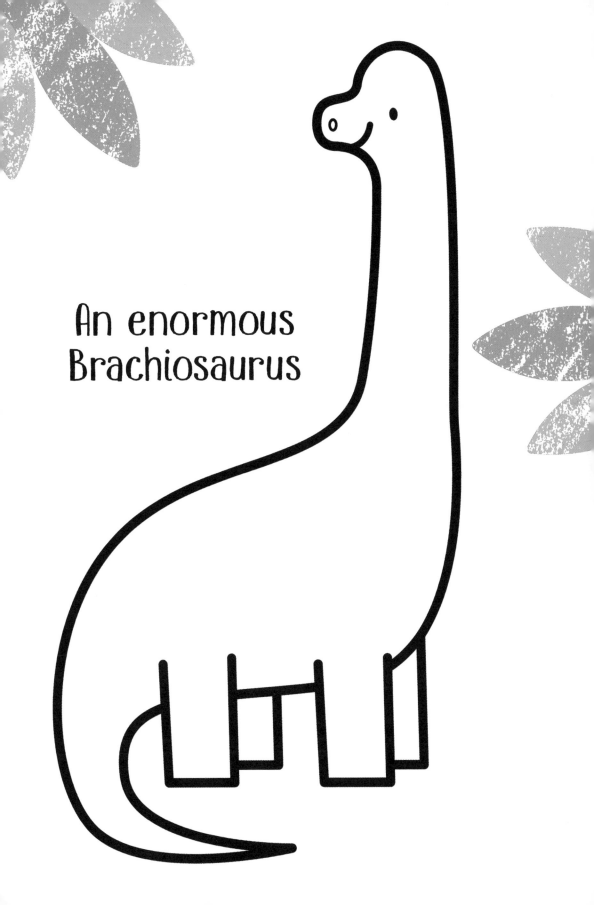

An enormous
Brachiosaurus

A tail-thwacking
Pinacosaurus

A short-beaked
Citipati

A motherly
Maiasaura

A toothy
Baryonyx

A long-beaked
Ornithocheirus

A speedy
Hypsilophodon

A sail-backed Spinosaurus

A toothless
Shonisaurus

A plant-eating
Protoceratops

A tail-swinging Euoplocephalus

A spiky-skulled
Stygimoloch

A soaring Quetzalcoatlus

A swishing-tailed Diplodocus

A sharp-clawed Therizinosaurus

A parrot-beaked Psittacosaurus

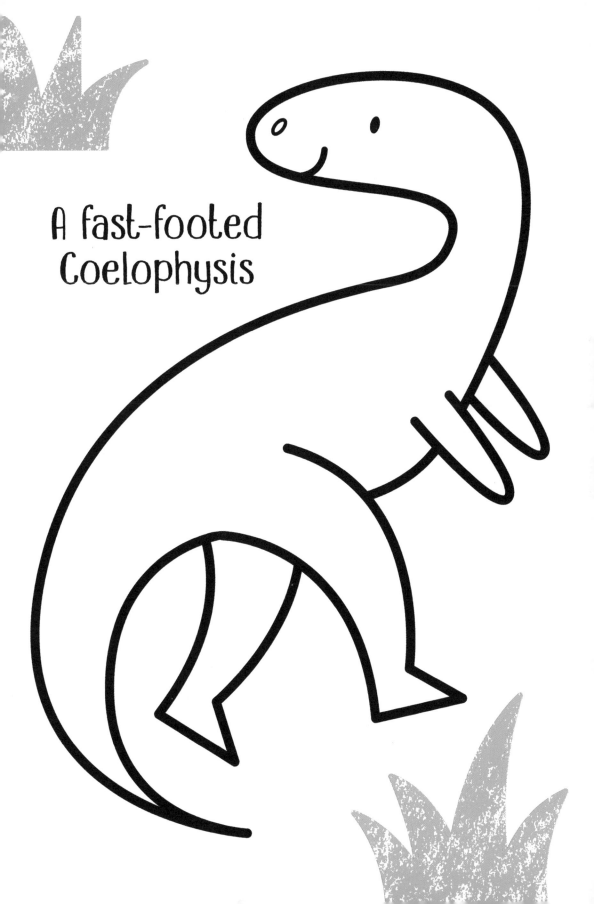

A fast-footed
Coelophysis

A fierce Ceratosaurus